WHAT'S THE POINT OF THIS BOOK?

I hope you enjoy working through this book. It took months of development and years of playing with ideas before that. **If you like it, please tell your friends and write a review on Amazon!** We are a family business: customer recommendations make an enormous difference.

This series grew out of my more exam-oriented resources in 11 Plus Lifeline. So many parents got in touch to ask for further writing materials, sometimes for exam preparation and sometimes just because their children enjoyed being creative, that I decided to to do something about it. I wanted the resources to be about more than exams, and I wanted them to be suitable for people all across the English-speaking world.

RSL Creative Writing focuses on descriptive writing and short stories, but the series also includes packs covering letters, emails and persuasive essays. There are even opportunities to continue a story by a famous author, blending your style with theirs.

The guiding idea behind this series is that a young person's creativity deserves respect. Far too often, children are taught to write childishly, with a focus on shortcuts: *use lots of adjectives, add these ten "wow words"*, and so on. However, I've found that many children can write as well as adults, if only they are shown how. By teaching them cheats rather than encouraging them to think about language in a mature way, grown-ups do them no favours.

Children should be shown the power of words. They should be taught that language is an enormous toolbox, full of possibilities but requiring careful judgment. The challenge we face is to choose words effectively, finding the best ways to shape our readers' thoughts and feelings.

Learning to write well involves learning to read well. Everybody finds it difficult to spot weaknesses in their own writing. For this reason, if we want to see things from a reader's point of view, it's best to start by looking at somebody else's work. That's why this book is full of examples. Mind you, not all of them are *good* examples!

Confident children will be able to use these resources independently. However, the series is likely to be even more useful when parents and children discuss things together … especially if both of you attempt the exercises and compare your answers. Try it! You may be surprised by the results.

Happy writing!

Robert

ALSO AVAILABLE

RSL Creative Writing: further volumes

11 Plus Lifeline (printable resources for all 11+ subjects):
www.11pluslifeline.com

RSL 11+ Comprehension

RSL 11+ Comprehension: Volume 2

RSL 11+ Maths

RSL 8+ to 10+ Comprehension

RSL 13+ Comprehension

GCSE Maths by RSL

GCSE Spanish by RSL

GCSE French by RSL

GCSE German by RSL

RSL Creative Writing: Book 2
by Robert Lomax

Published by RSL Educational Ltd

Company 10793232
VAT 252515326
17 Woodside Road, Bricket Wood, St Albans
Registered in England & Wales

Design and typesetting by
Heather Macpherson at Raspberry Creative Type
Printed by Short Run Press Limited, Exeter

www.rsleducational.co.uk

CONTENTS

youtube.com/c/Easy11Plus

HOW TO USE THEM WELL

This pack will help you use adjectives more effectively.

ADJECTIVES

This pack will help you use adjectives more effectively.

- When is an adjective most useful?
- How do you choose which one is best?
- How many should you use?

An adjective describes a noun or a pronoun.

A noun is a word such as "**phone**", "**Henry**" (a proper noun) or "**excitement**" (an abstract noun), referring to a thing – whether or not this thing has a real presence in the world and could be touched with your hand.

A pronoun *replaces a noun*, doing the same job in a sentence. "Henry **uses the phone**" can become "He **uses the phone**" if you use the pronoun "**he**". Adding another pronoun to replace "**the phone**", it could become "He **uses** it".

Here are some examples of adjectives:

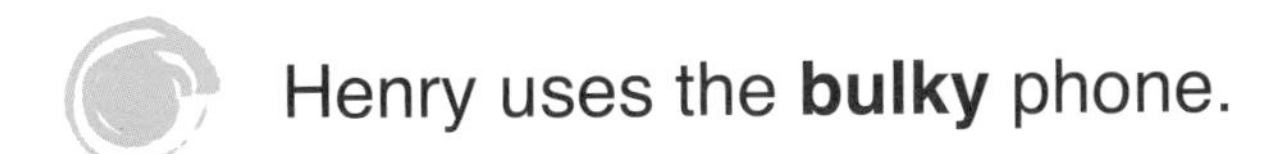

- Henry uses the **bulky** phone.
- He is **short**.
- They are **argumentative**.
- She felt **fierce** anger.

Here's a paragraph from Pack 3, with the adjectives highlighted:

> Something <u>cold</u> was scraping my face and I could smell <u>damp</u> turf. The ground beneath my body was <u>spongy</u>, moulding itself to the pressure of my chest.

When adjectives are listed, it's normal to separate them with commas.

Don't write:

"**She lay on the cool damp clammy ground**".

Do write:

"**She lay on the cool, damp, clammy ground**".

When two words combine to become an adjective, conveying a single concept, they become a compound adjective and need a hyphen.

"**She looked at the still, blue water**" means that the water was still (not moving) and *blue*.

"**She looked at the still-blue water**" means that the water *hadn't changed colour yet*.

"**She looked at the still blue water**" is unclear: you need to choose one of the options above.

Bear in mind that when you modify an adjective with an adverb ending in "**-ly**" ("**the rapidly spreading stench**"), you don't use a hyphen.

HOW ADJECTIVES CHANGE MEANING

Here is an extract from *The Jungle Book*, by Rudyard Kipling – with a few changes:

A shadow dropped down into the circle. It was Bagheera the Panther. Everybody knew Bagheera. He was like a buffalo, like an elephant. He had a voice like honey dripping from a tree, and skin like down.

This pack is all about adjectives, and in the extract above, I've removed all of them. It seems rather empty.

Here's the same extract, with Kipling's adjectives added back in. I've highlighted them for you:

A *black* shadow dropped down into the circle. It was Bagheera the *Black* Panther. Everybody knew Bagheera. He was *cunning*, as *bold* as the *wild* buffalo, and as *reckless* as the *wounded* elephant. He had a voice as *soft* as *wild* honey dripping from a tree, and a skin *softer* than down.

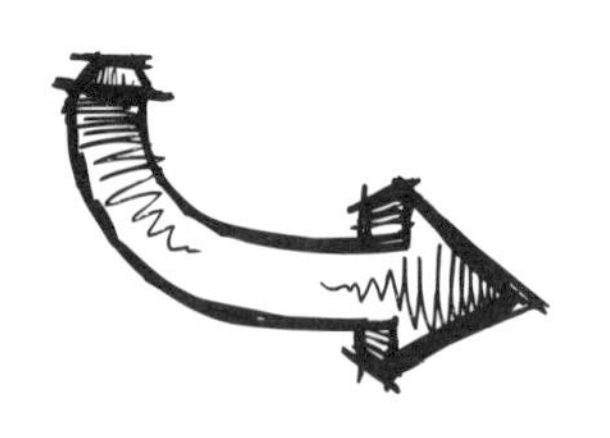

Adjectives make an enormous difference! The choices that you make can completely change the meaning of a text.

Let's see whether I can make Bagheera seem harmless, just by changing some of the adjectives:

> A *fuzzy* shadow dropped down into the circle. It was Bagheera the *Black* Panther. Everybody knew Bagheera. He was *awkward*, as *unreliable* as the *lost* buffalo, and as *doddery* as the *new-born* elephant. He had a voice as *uncertain* as *lumpy* honey dripping from a tree, and a skin *more tangled* than down.

These changes haven't just shifted the emphasis of the paragraph:

they have turned Bagheera from a fearsome and sly predator into a figure of fun.

EXERCISE 1: USING ADJECTIVES TO CHANGE MEANING

Now it's your turn! You don't need to change every adjective. Often "Bagheera the Black Panther" will be fine, while "skin softer than down" will be appropriate in many contexts.

Fill in the gaps with adjectives to make Bagheera seem kind and friendly.

A .... shadow dropped down into the circle. It was Bagheera the .... Panther. Everybody knew Bagheera. He was .... as .... as the .... buffalo, and as .... as the .... elephant. He had a voice as .... as .... honey dripping from a tree, and a skin .... than down.

Can you make him seem utterly evil **– more so than in Kipling's version?**

A .... shadow dropped down into the circle. It was Bagheera the .... Panther. Everybody knew Bagheera. He was .... as .... as the .... buffalo, and as .... as the .... elephant. He had a voice as .... as .... honey dripping from a tree, and a skin .... than down.

Now use your imagination to do something different! Whatever you aim to do, try to create a picture of Bagheera that fits together.

Don't make him sneaky in one sentence and trustworthy in another!

A.................. shadow dropped down into the circle. It was Bagheera the.................. Panther. Everybody knew Bagheera. He was .... as .... as the .... buffalo, and as .... as the .... elephant. He had a voice as .... as .... honey dripping from a tree, and a skin .... than down.

EXERCISE 1: EXAMPLE ANSWERS

Fill in the gaps with adjectives to make Bagheera seem kind and friendly.

A *soft-edged* shadow dropped down into the circle. It was Bagheera the *kindly* Panther. Everybody knew Bagheera. He was *wise*, as *solid* as the *standing* buffalo, and as *dependable* as the *ancient* elephant. He had a voice as *loving* as *warm* honey dripping from a tree, and a skin *softer* than down.

Can you make him seem utterly evil – more so than in Kipling's version?

A *menacing* shadow dropped down into the circle. It was Bagheera the *Black* Panther. Everybody knew Bagheera. He was *cruel*, as *deadly* as the *sharp-horned* buffalo, and as *implacable* as the *rampaging* elephant. He had a voice as *harsh* as *sour* honey dripping from a tree, and a skin *slicker* than down.

EXERCISE 2: HOW MANY ADJECTIVES IS TOO MANY?

Here's some science fiction writing by Marko, a student:

The enormous, lumbering ship eased itself into calm orbit, bright sunlight flashing from curved hull panels as its colossal bulk twisted then settled into steady, perfect alignment. Beneath it the awesome planet rolled, impossibly vast, specked with the dark, mysterious craters of tremendous asteroid impacts. Tight little gas clouds scudded across its ruddy surface, and between them roamed menacing, thousand-metre spaceships, reduced to the scale of insignificant mosquitos.

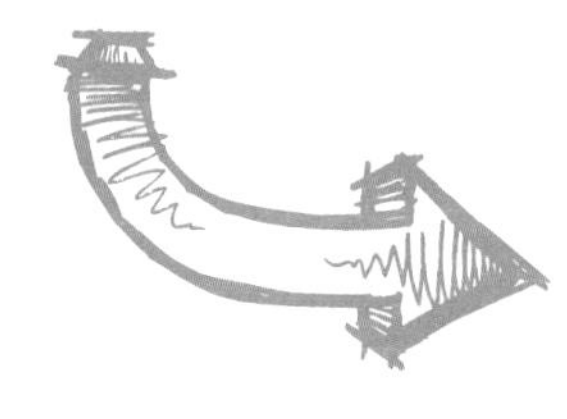

We can probably agree that there are too many adjectives here! The paragraph is quite as heavy and lumbering as the spaceships it describes.

Some of these adjectives state things that the reader will be able to work out, or at least guess, from the rest of the writing.

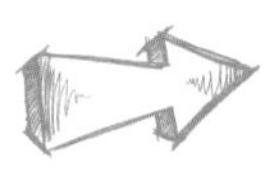

The paragraph is repeated below. Cross out **just those adjectives giving information that the reader can probably work out for themselves**. Use a **pencil** (so that you can change your mind) and cross out with straight lines, like this: ~~adjective~~.

My answer follows straight afterwards, so you might like to cover it before you begin.

> The enormous, lumbering ship eased itself into calm orbit, bright sunlight flashing from curved hull panels as its colossal bulk twisted then settled into steady, perfect alignment. Beneath it the awesome planet rolled, impossibly vast, specked with the dark, mysterious craters of tremendous asteroid impacts. Tight little gas clouds scudded across its ruddy surface, and between them roamed menacing, thousand-metre spaceships, reduced to the scale of insignificant mosquitos.

Here is my suggested answer:

> The ~~enormous, lumbering~~ ship eased itself into ~~calm~~ orbit, ~~bright~~ sunlight flashing from curved hull panels as its ~~colossal~~ bulk twisted then settled into ~~steady~~, perfect alignment. Beneath it the ~~awesome~~ planet rolled, impossibly vast, specked with the dark, mysterious craters of tremendous asteroid impacts. Tight little gas clouds scudded across its ruddy surface, and between them roamed menacing, thousand-metre spaceships, reduced to the scale of ~~insignificant~~ mosquitos.

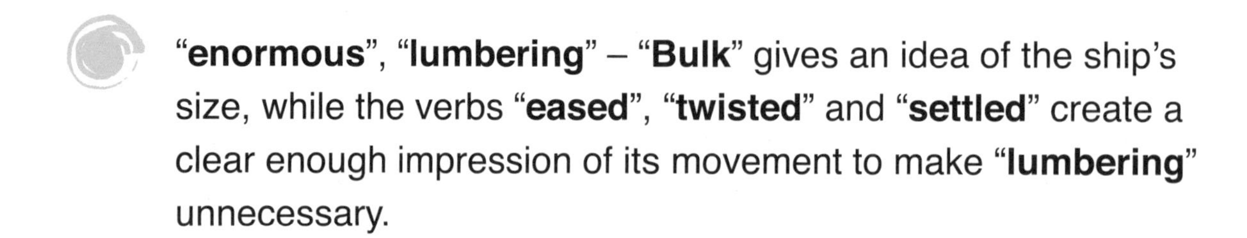

- "**enormous**", "**lumbering**" – "**Bulk**" gives an idea of the ship's size, while the verbs "**eased**", "**twisted**" and "**settled**" create a clear enough impression of its movement to make "**lumbering**" unnecessary.

- "**calm**", "**bright**", "**colossal**" and "**steady**" – All these ideas are clearly implied by the rest of the sentence.

- "**awesome**" – ***Show, don't tell*** is a good rule: readers usually want to draw their own conclusions, not be told what to feel. In this case, the rest of the sentence does the job very well already. If a reader doesn't find this scene awesome, they aren't making an imaginative effort!

- "**Insignificant**" – The whole point of comparing the ships to mosquitos is to show how insignificant they seem. It doesn't need to be stated.

Now return to the paragraph with your crossing out. This time, cross out **any other adjectives** that you think could be left out to make the paragraph more effective. Cross out with squiggly lines, like this: adjective.

Once again, here is my suggested answer. My judgements here are personal, and – as you will see – there's plenty of room to make different choices:

The ~~enormous, lumbering~~ ship eased itself into ~~calm~~ orbit, ~~bright~~ sunlight flashing from curved hull panels as its ~~colossal~~ bulk twisted then settled into ~~steady~~, ~~perfect~~ alignment. Beneath it the ~~awesome~~ planet rolled, impossibly vast, specked with the dark, ~~mysterious~~ craters of ~~tremendous~~ asteroid impacts. Tight little gas clouds scudded across its ~~muddy~~ surface, and between them roamed ~~menacing~~, thousand-metre spaceships, reduced to the scale of ~~insignificant~~ mosquitos.

"**perfect**" – The important information is that an enormous ship lines itself up in orbit. Exactly how precise this alignment is may not make much difference to the reader's impression of events. If it is where it should be and in good "**alignment**", that's what matters.

"**mysterious**" – I usually prefer not to tell a reader what to think or feel. If they want to find the dark craters "**mysterious**", that's up to them. At any rate, it's a strange word to use, because the reason for the craters is given straight afterwards.

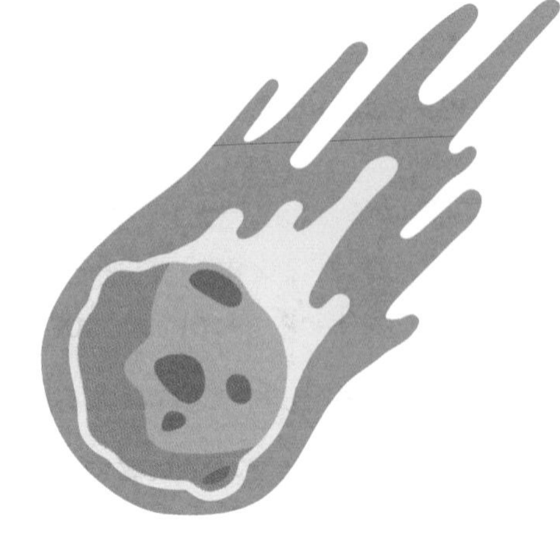

- "**tremendous**" – An asteroid strike doesn't have to be "**tremendous**"; but unless they are told otherwise, a reader is likely to assume that it is. This word could also have been crossed out at the previous stage.
- "**ruddy**" – This is likely to be my most controversial choice! In my view, this sentence is mainly about the clouds and the spaceships, and I don't want to distract the reader by trying to create a picture of the planet's surface too. This could have been included in the previous sentence. I also like the "**s**" sounds of "**gas clouds scudded across its surface**", and another word in the middle spoils the effect.
- "**menacing**" – "**Roamed**", and the reference to the ships' size, already implies this, but in a subtler and more interesting way.

Here's the paragraph after my edits:

The ship eased itself into orbit, sunlight flashing from curved hull panels as its bulk twisted then settled into alignment. Beneath it the planet rolled, impossibly vast, specked with the dark craters of asteroid impacts. Tight little gas clouds scudded across its surface, and between them roamed thousand-metre spaceships, reduced to the scale of mosquitos.

This paragraph is still very descriptive, yet contains relatively few adjectives. Here it is again, with the survivors highlighted:

The ship eased itself into orbit, sunlight flashing from curved hull panels as its bulk twisted then settled into alignment. Beneath it the planet rolled, impossibly vast, specked with the dark craters of asteroid impacts. Tight little gas clouds scudded across its surface, and between them roamed thousand-metre spaceships, reduced to the scale of mosquitos.

You may notice that the remaining adjectives are some of the simplest ones from the original paragraph, while the longer, more complex words have been deleted.

Unusual or complex adjectives aren't bad, so long as they are used appropriately. However, **everyday words often contribute to the most powerful descriptions**.

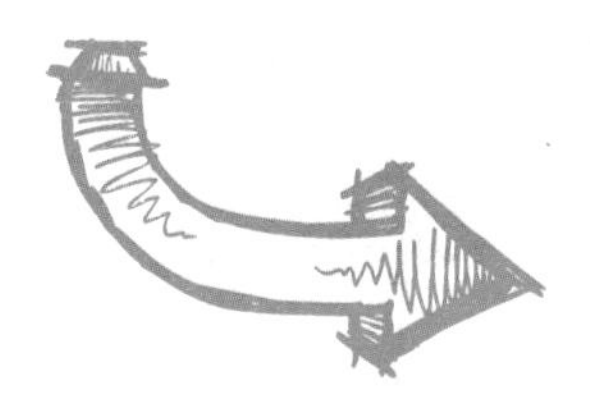

How does my finished paragraph compare to yours?

EXERCISE 3: ADDING ADJECTIVES

**Here are two short passages for you to improve by adding adjectives as appropriate.
Write your new version in the space provided.**

Only add adjectives that make the writing more effective: a light scattering is likely to be enough.

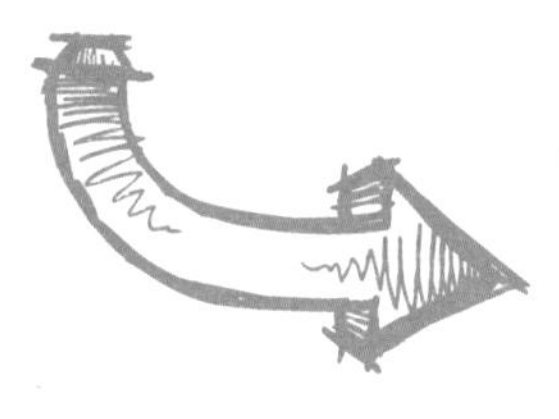

Remember that simple adjectives are sometimes more effective than unusual ones.

You can make other small changes if these are needed to fit an adjective in: for instance, "**Katie helps her sister**" could become "**Katie** ***is generous and*** **helps her sister**".

The bicycle skidded down the track, throwing up rocks and twigs. Edward grasped the handlebars, clenching his teeth, his face full of concentration.

....

....

....

....

....

The bear sat in the shade, using its teeth to dig tangles from its fur. It flexed its claws and let out a yawn, then rolled backwards against a tree. Within seconds, it was asleep.

....

....

....

....

....

EXERCISE 3: EXAMPLE ANSWERS

I've highlighted my changes in each case.

The bicycle skidded down the track, throwing up rocks and twigs. Edward grasped the handlebars, clenching his teeth, his face full of concentration.

The **rickety** bicycle skidded down the track, throwing up rocks and **splintered** twigs. Edward grasped the handlebars, clenching his teeth, his **sweaty** face full of concentration.

Here's a different version:

The bicycle skidded down the **murderous** track, throwing up rocks and twigs. Edward grasped the **stocky** handlebars, clenching his teeth, his face full of **fierce** concentration.

The bear sat in the shade, using its teeth to dig tangles from its fur. It flexed its claws and let out a yawn, then rolled backwards against a tree. Within seconds, it was asleep.

The bear sat in the **balmy** shade, using its teeth to dig tangles from its **matted** fur. It flexed its claws and let out a **languid** yawn, then rolled backwards against a tree. Within seconds, it was asleep.

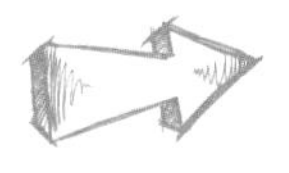

The problem with this response is that the "**adjective-noun-comma**" pattern becomes a bit repetitive, with "**balmy shade, using**" being followed by "**languid yawn, then**".

The following solution avoids this problem:

The **elderly** bear sat in the shade, using its teeth to dig **dense** tangles from its fur. It flexed its claws and let out a **languid** yawn, then rolled backwards against a tree. Within seconds, it was **in a profound sleep**.

HAD ENOUGH OF ADJECTIVES?

I would guess that the last exercise was at least a little frustrating! When you can only describe using adjectives, your options are limited.

Here are a few other techniques that you might use instead (or as well):

More interesting verbs: **"The bear sprawled in the shade"**

Adverbs: **"The bear sat contentedly in the shade"**

Simile: **"The bear sat in the shade like a Buddha"**

Metaphor: **"his face a flushed balloon, swollen with concentration"**

Personification: **"[the bike was] excitedly flinging rocks and twigs into the tree-line"**

EXERCISE 4: ALL-OUT DESCRIPTION

Now have another go with the bear and the bicycle. This time, you can use whatever descriptive devices you want!

Think carefully about whether to use an adjective, or another technique, in each case.

Which criteria do you use to decide?

How often is an adjective the best choice?

The bicycle skidded down the track, throwing up rocks and twigs. Edward grasped the handlebars, clenching his teeth, his face full of concentration.

....

....

....

....

....

The bear sat in the shade, using its teeth to dig tangles from its fur. It flexed its claws and let out a yawn, then rolled backwards against a tree. Within seconds, it was asleep.

FOLLOW-UP EXERCISE

Describe the following scene in three different ways, experimenting with a range of descriptive techniques including the use of adjectives.

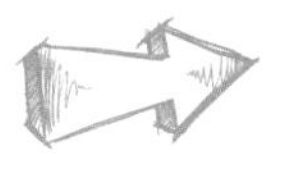

Try to write well: think about when **not to** describe things, as well as when to do so.

A Bar at the Folies-Bergère by Édouard Manet

First Description

....

....

....

....

....

....

....

....

....

Second Description

....

....

....

....

....

....

....

....

....

Third Description

blank page

WRITING TO PERSUADE

This pack will show you how to argue effectively in a letter or email.

EMAILS AND LETTERS

This pack will show you how to argue effectively in a letter or email.

You've probably written a lot of letters and emails in your life.

But have you ever thought about what these letters and emails all have in common?

Whenever you write to somebody, you are trying to persuade them.

You might be persuading them …

- to change their opinion about something.
- to do something that you want them to.
- to like you.
- to explain something.
- to believe that you are grateful/angry/something else.

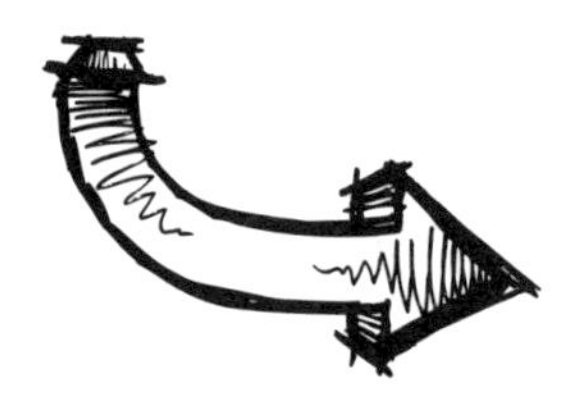

There are other possibilities!

Once you think about writing in terms of persuasion, it changes the way that you go about it.

HOW TO BE PERSUASIVE

We're going to look at two short emails. Which one would be more likely to persuade you?

Hi Andy,

Please lend me £200.

Kind regards,

Susan

If Andy doesn't already want to lend Susan £500, this is unlikely to make him change his mind! In fact, because the message is so blunt and demanding, it might make him even more certain about not paying her than he was before.

Compare this email:

Hi Andy,

I'm sorry for the delay since I was last in touch.

Last year I lent you £100 to help you buy a new bike. You paid it back quickly, which I really appreciated.

Now I'm short of cash to buy a bike for myself. I wonder whether you might be able to help me out this time, by lending me £200?

I'm due to receive £500 from my grandma at the end of the month, so I will be able to pay you back soon. Indeed, this will be my first priority when I have Gran's money.

I don't plan to keep asking for loans: this is a one-off.

Even if you aren't able to help, I hope we can meet up soon.

Kind regards,

Susan

Susan has given considerable thought to persuading Andy, and she does this without trying to bully him.

Most importantly, she has thought carefully about why Andy might not want to lend her the money: her whole message is shaped by this thought.

She answers this by saying that she will have the money to repay him soon, and promises that this will be her "**first priority**".

He might worry that she will keep asking for more.

She makes clear that this request is a "**one-off**".

He might wonder why it's his job to help.

She points out that she helped him in the past – but focuses on thanking him for his speedy repayment, rather than creating pressure by saying I HELPED YOU, SO YOU HAVE TO HELP ME!

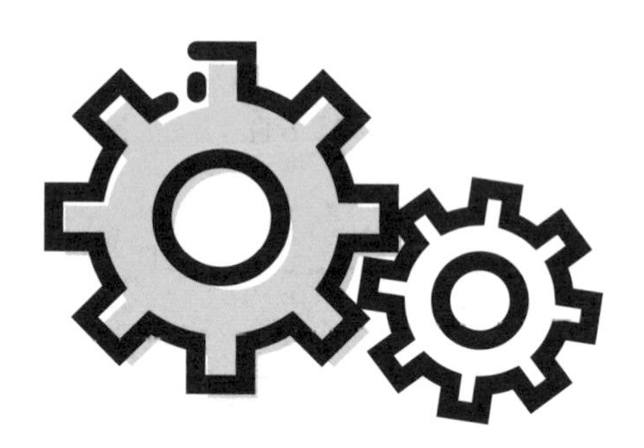

He might worry that she only sees this friendship as a way to get money.

She starts with a friendly apology for not being in touch more, and ends by making clear that she values his friendship even if he can't help out.

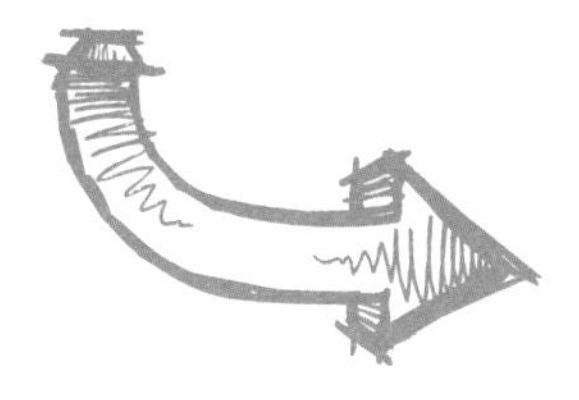

Andy is much more likely to agree if he receives the second email than if he receives the first!

The key to persuading somebody is to think about **their point of view** at least as much as you think about your own.

HOW ARE LETTERS DIFFERENT FROM EMAILS?

This pack will focus on emails, because you are likely to write many more of them in your life.

If you need to write a letter instead, it's likely to look like this:

15 Roady Road
Bucket Hill
BH5 5HB

This is your address. In a formal letter, you would write the recipient's address after yours.

05/07/2026

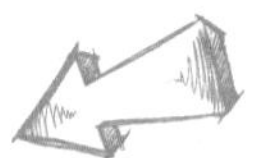

If you don't know their name, write "**Dear Sir**", "**Dear Madam**" or "**Dear Sir/Madam**".

Dear Ms Doesntexist,

When addressing a woman in a formal letter, it's usual to write "**Ms**" unless you're certain that they prefer "**Miss**" or "**Mrs**".

This is a letter. I hope you enjoy reading it as much as I've enjoyed writing it. It is very lettery, and contains many words that serve no purpose other than to occupy space. I hope you feel as well informed after reading it as before.

Yours sincerely,

T. Imewaster

In a formal letter, end with "**Yours sincerely**" if you started with a name ("**Dear Mrs Doesntexist**"), or "**Yours faithfully**" if you wrote "**Dear Madam**". In a letter to a person you know, you might sign off with "**Kind regards**" or "**Best wishes**" (both of which are also common ways to end an email) – or even "**Love**", if you know them very well indeed!

Some of these things can also apply to formal emails: for instance, writing something like "**Dear Sir/Madam**" when you don't know a person's name, or using "**Ms**" rather than "**Miss**" or "**Mrs**" with a woman's surname when you aren't sure what they prefer.

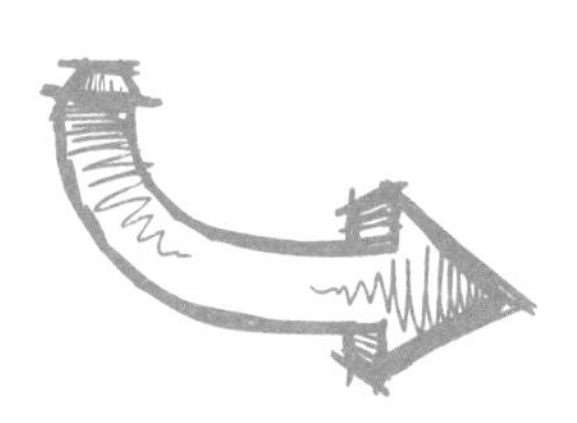

While you might say "Hi" or "Hello" at the start of an informal email, letters almost always begin with "Dear".

YOUR TURN!

Here's your task:

Write an **email** to your local Member of Parliament (MP), Melinda Thrubbock, asking her to support your plan for a new international airport near your house.

If you don't live in the UK and don't have an MP, feel free to choose whatever sort of political representative makes sense!

Before you write your email, you'll need to think carefully about what you are aiming to achieve and how you want to go about it.

Think about the following questions and take brief notes in the spaces provided.

1. What are you actually trying to achieve? What is the main thing that you want your MP to do after reading your message?

2. What are your main reasons for wanting an international airport near to your house? Think about how it would benefit other people, not just you!

3 Why might some local people object to your idea?

....

....

....

....

....

....

....

....

4 How would you respond to local people's objections?

....

....

....

....

....

....

....

....

5 Why might some people in the rest of the country object to your idea?

....

....

....

....

....

....

....

....

6 How would you respond to these people's objections?

....

....

....

....

....

....

....

....

7. Why else might your MP not be keen to help you? For example, might she feel that she has more important things to deal with?

....

....

....

....

....

....

....

....

8. How would you respond to your MP's own objections? How would it benefit her to support this project? (Don't try to bribe her!)

....

....

....

....

....

....

....

....

9 Are there any things that you need to take special care to avoid doing in this email?

....

....

....

....

....

....

....

....

These nine questions don't form a plan: a good email won't go through them from 1 to 9! However, they may not be too far away from your email's eventual structure, either.

A clear layout for a persuasive email will probably look something like this:

- A polite introduction that makes clear why you are getting in touch with this particular person, and – in broad terms – what you are trying to achieve.

- Your main argument(s).

- Your response to the most likely objections (those that your main argument hasn't already dealt with).

- A conclusion that suggests what the next steps might be, if your reader agrees.

Once you're happy with your answers to questions 1 to 9, write your email in the space below – or, as it's an email, you might prefer to type your answer and print it out!

....

....

....

....

....

....

....

....

....

....

ABDUR'S ANSWER

Read Abdur's answers to the questions, then his email.

- How do his notes (answers) carry across into his email?
- What do you like about his work and what do you dislike?
- In what ways is his email similar to yours?
- How is it different?

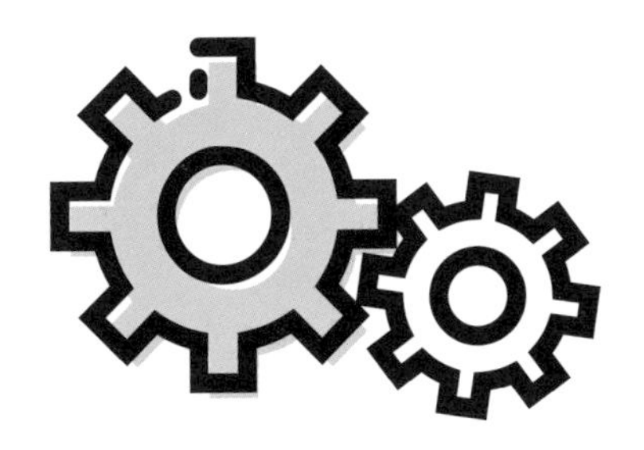

1 What are you actually trying to achieve? What is the main thing that you want your MP to do after reading your message?

I want her to persuade other politicians to support a new airport in the fields beside the river near my house.

2 What are your main reasons for wanting an international airport near to your house? Think about how it would benefit other people, not just you!

Likely to bring tourists to the area. Would encourage economic growth: new connections for local businesses; new businesses might come to the area; convenient for overseas businesses to invest money here. Would also widen cultural diversity and awareness, e.g. by making it easier for young people to experience other cultures through visits abroad.

3 Why might some local people object to your idea?

Don't want to lose the fields to an airport; worried about noise and pollution.

4 How would you respond to local people's objections?

With money from airport, could improve other underused parks and outdoor spaces. Would not be a major airport like Heathrow.

5 Why might some people in the rest of the country object to your idea?

This could take business away from other airports. It might cost a lot to build.

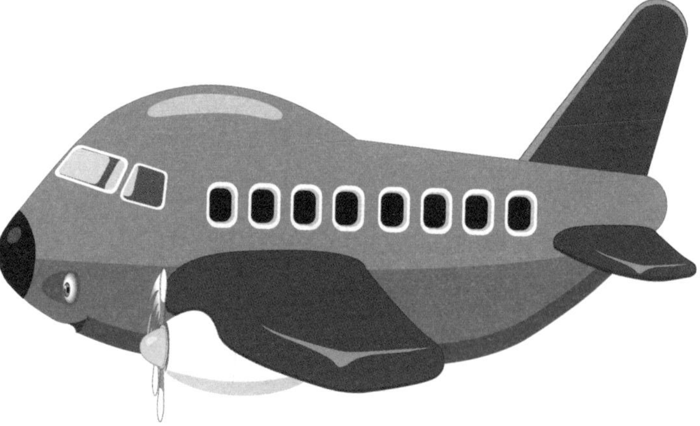

6 How would you respond to these people's objections?

Some other airports are already too busy: this can lighten loads for them. An airport here should bring in much more than it costs.

7 Why else might your MP not be keen to help you? For example, might she feel that she has more important things to deal with?

Might feel is not a good use of her time. Might not want to get caught in a messy local debate.

8 How would you respond to your MP's own objections? How would it benefit her to support this project? (Don't try to bribe her!)

There should be widespread local support, because could make a big difference for the area. Subtly flatter her by saying that her support would make a crucial difference!

9 Are there any things that you need to take special care to avoid doing in this email?

Don't explain the obvious or lecture her. Don't let points be vague or long-winded: politicians are busy people.

Dear Ms Thrubbock,

I'm contacting you about a proposal that would bring significant benefits to Ulverston and the surrounding area.

There is an area of land near the river that would be an ideal site for a new international airport. After research and consultation, I have no doubt that the economic and social impact would be overwhelmingly positive. Bearing in mind your local influence and your role in Parliament, your support for the project would be invaluable and perhaps decisive.

Ulverston is some distance from the nearest major airport, which means that local businesses do not benefit from easy international connections. An airport here would not only provide a boost for existing businesses, making it easy for them to sell and invest overseas: it would also attract investment from other UK and international companies.

By making it easy for visitors to arrive from abroad, the airport would benefit the local tourist economy - both by making Ulverston a destination in its own right, and by making it the main stop-over point for people on their way to the hills of the Lake District.

Taking all these factors into account, I am confident that the airport would cover its costs quickly and remain profitable for many decades: something that would be reflected in significant tax revenues for local and national government.

Aside from economic considerations, a new airport would widen local people's horizons. Schools would find it easier and cheaper to arrange trips overseas. Language exchange students would see Ulverston as a natural destination - and they would go home enthused by the wonders of the Cumbrian coastline, ready to share their discoveries with family and friends.

The airport could deliver all these benefits while operating on a fairly small scale: without becoming a major hub, and without generating excessive noise and air pollution. Meanwhile, it would improve life for people near to existing airports such as Manchester and Birmingham, taking on some of the flights that currently make the skies around them so overcrowded.

I am aware that some people in Ulverston don't like the idea of losing so much land near the river, which is crossed by some popular footpaths. However, residents understand how beneficial the income from a new airport might be. My strong impression is that people are open to the idea, so long as they know that money will be invested in improving local parks and other public spaces, and in making the town a more pleasant place to live. If the arguments are clearly and honestly presented, and particularly if somebody with your influence is involved in making the case, I do not foresee significant local opposition.

Please let me know if you would like more detail about any aspects of this proposal.

Kind regards,

Abdur Rahman

ABDUR'S EMAIL: SECTION BY SECTION

Dear Ms Thrubbock,

I'm contacting you about a proposal that would bring significant benefits to Ulverston and the surrounding area.

Abdur doesn't launch straight in like this:

Dear Ms Thrubbock,

I'm contacting you to suggest that you support a new international airport in Ulverston.

If a reader's response to your very first line is to think "No, I disagree," you're likely to undermine your chance of persuading them later on.

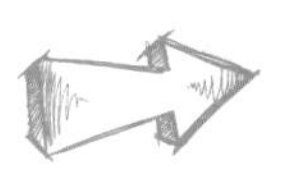

On the other hand, if you start with something that it's easy to go along with – such as "**bringing benefits**" to the local area – you lay a good foundation for your more controversial ideas.

Abdur is right not to spend any longer than he does before talking about the airport. **It's a good thing that he didn't start like this:**

Dear Ms Thrubbock,

I'm contacting you about a proposal that would bring significant benefits to Ulverston and the surrounding area. It's a very interesting proposal, if I do say so myself, and I would encourage you to give it full consideration. My suggestion is likely to make a real difference - not only for local people, but for people across the UK.

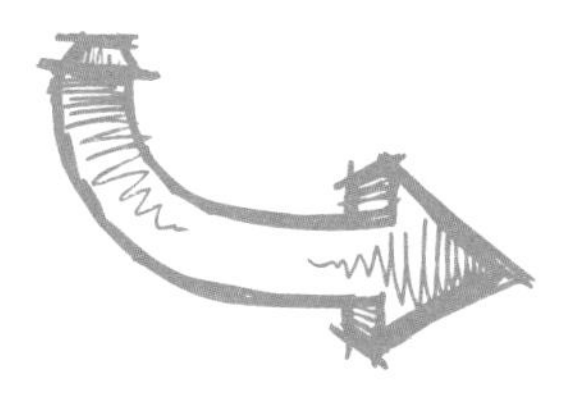

You don't want to sound as though you are embarrassed about your proposal – and busy people don't respond well to time-wasting waffle!

There is an area of land near the river that would be an ideal site for a new international airport. After research and consultation, I have no doubt that the economic and social impact would be overwhelmingly positive. Bearing in mind your local influence and your role in Parliament, your support for the project would be invaluable and perhaps decisive.

In this paragraph, Abdur …

- summarises his proposal in a single, short sentence;
- summarises the research that he has already done;
- explains why he is contacting this particular person.

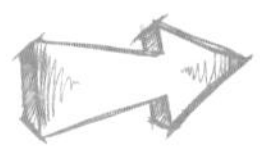

These are all things that he will explain more fully later. This paragraph acts as a sort of guide to the rest of his email. It may also help to bring his MP on-side, by showing that Abdur has a clear idea of what he is aiming for and why.

Ulverston is some distance from the nearest major airport, which means that local businesses do not benefit from easy international connections. An airport here would not only provide a boost for existing businesses, making it easy for them to sell and invest overseas: it would also attract investment from other UK and international companies.

By making it easy for visitors to arrive from abroad, the airport would benefit the local tourist economy - both by making Ulverston a destination in its own right, and by making it the main stop-over point for people on their way to the hills of the Lake District.

Taking all these factors into account, I am confident that the airport would cover its costs quickly and remain profitable for many decades: something that would be reflected in significant tax revenues for local and national government.

Aside from economic considerations, a new airport would widen local people's horizons. Schools would find it easier and cheaper to arrange trips overseas. Language exchange students would see Ulverston as a natural destination - and they would go home enthused by the wonders of the Cumbrian coastline, ready to share their discoveries with family and friends.

The airport could deliver all these benefits while operating on a fairly small scale: without becoming a major hub, and without generating excessive noise and air pollution. Meanwhile, it would improve life for people near to existing airports such as Manchester and Birmingham, taking on some of the flights that currently make the skies around them so overcrowded.

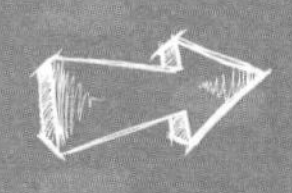

Notice how this section presents the positive case for the airport while casually knocking out various likely counter-arguments. The airport won't lose money: it will make money. It won't cause problems for local people or encourage resentment from people living near to other airports.

Abdur uses paragraphs to break his argument into clear sections:

- Business
- Tourism
- Profitability and tax revenue
- Cultural benefits
- Airport traffic and pollution

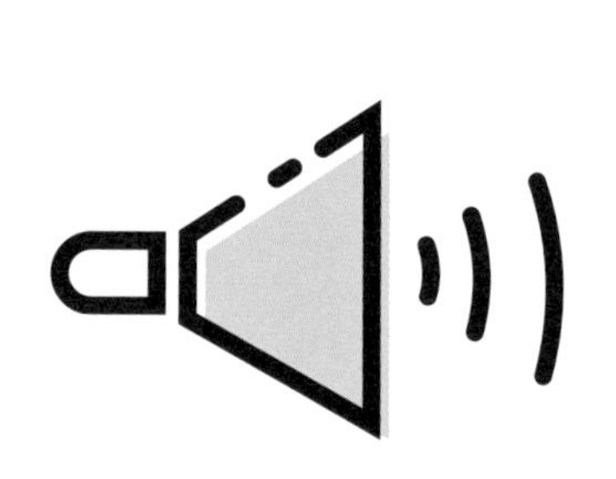

It's very important not to allow your ideas to become jumbled, or to let them crush in on one another so that some lose their importance.

All these ideas are addressed succinctly: some in only a single sentence. They may not be detailed enough to convince somebody who already has a contrary opinion. **However, Abdur's clarity and confidence suggest that more detailed explanations can be provided if required.**

I am aware that some people in Ulverston don't like the idea of losing so much land near the river, which is crossed by some popular footpaths. However, residents understand how beneficial the income from a new airport might be. My strong impression is that people are open to the idea, so long as they know that money will be invested in improving local parks and other public spaces, and in making the town a more pleasant place to live. If the arguments are clearly and honestly presented, and particularly if somebody with your influence is involved in making the case, I do not foresee significant local opposition.

This paragraph starts by admitting a likely downside that Ms Thrubbock may not yet be aware of – but which would certainly come to light later on, if she researched the idea herself. By raising a sticking point, while also setting out a clear plan to address it, Abdur shows that he has thought about his proposal in depth.

Abdur makes clear one way in which Ms Thrubbock can help: by being an influential voice, addressing and allaying local concerns. There's no chance that she will finish the letter and ask herself, "**But what exactly does he expect me to do?**"

Please let me know if you would like more detail about any aspects of this proposal.

Kind regards,

Abdur Rahman

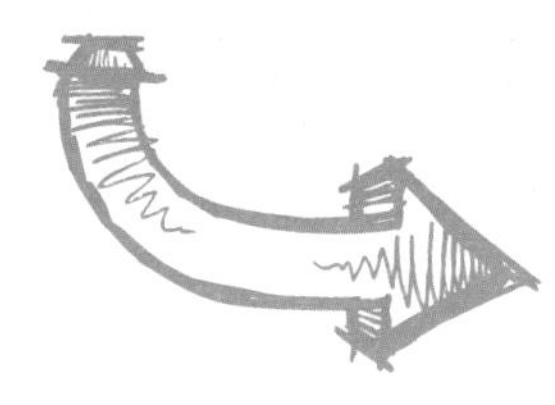

The email ends courteously, without being pushy.

Compare these alternatives:

I hope you'll agree with me that this is an excellent proposal.

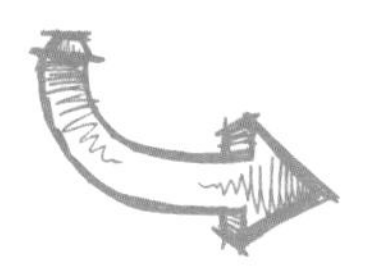

This seems arrogant, as well as pushy. It would be more likely to annoy Abdur's MP than to persuade her.

As you can see, there are both advantages and disadvantages to my proposal. However, I'm confident that the advantages win out.

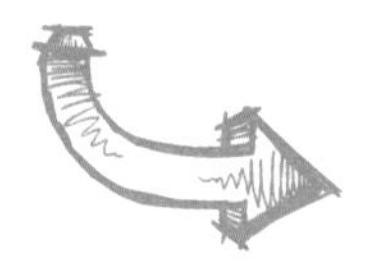

This is a bit wishy-washy. An ending like this would suggest that Abdur is less confident than he claims to be.

It would also undermine the argument in the rest of his email. The message up to this point has been that there are many advantages, and that where people may have worries, these are either mistaken or can be addressed. However, this alternative conclusion would imply that some downsides are unavoidable.

Instead of making a closing argument, Abdur ends with an offer of further information. This shows respect, by making clear that the letter's recipient is in control of what happens next.

If Abdur's email has given you some new ideas, it may be worth having another go!

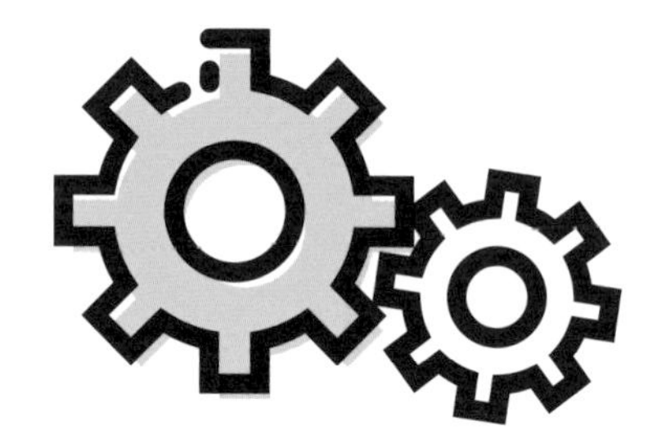

FOLLOW-UP TASK

Write an email to your Head Teacher, asking them to arrange a year group trip to your nearest zoo.

ZOO

blank page

CONTINUING A STORY

This pack will show you how to continue a story by another writer – and how not to do it!

THE TIME MACHINE

This pack will show you how to continue a story by another writer – and how not to do it!

Continuing a story is a common creative writing task, **and it's a brilliant exercise.**

Rather than inventing your own setting and characters, you need to think about what a well-known writer has done, why they have done it – and of course, how.

This requires you to understand somebody else's writing thoroughly, and apply that understanding to your own work.

What are the story's main themes and ideas?

Where are the events set? What atmosphere does this setting create?

What directions might the plot take, while remaining believable?

What are the characters like? How do they think and feel? How do they respond to things?

What is the author's writing style? How can you mesh it with your own, so that your continuation seems natural?

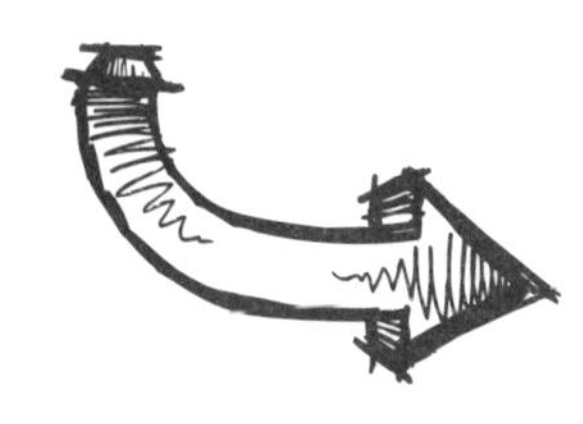

Continuing another person's work is one of the best ways to explore alternative ways of writing and develop your own skills.

READING PASSAGE

The following text is adapted from *The Time Machine* by H.G. Wells, published in 1895.

It was at ten o'clock today that the first of all time machines began its career. I gave it a last tap, tried all the screws again, put one more drop of oil on the quartz rod, and sat myself in the saddle. I took the starting lever in one hand and the stopping one in the other, pressed the first, and almost immediately the second. I seemed to reel; I felt a nightmare sensation of falling; and, looking round, I saw the laboratory exactly as before. Had anything happened? For a moment I suspected that my intellect had tricked me. Then I noted the clock. A moment before, as it seemed, it had stood at a minute or so past ten; now it was nearly half-past three!

I drew a breath, set my teeth, gripped the starting lever with both hands, and went off with a thud. The laboratory got hazy and went dark. Mrs Watchett came in and walked, apparently without seeing me, towards the garden door. I suppose it took her a minute or so to traverse the place, but to me she seemed to shoot across the room like a rocket. I pressed the lever over to its extreme position. The night came like the turning out of a lamp, and in another moment came tomorrow. The laboratory grew faint and hazy, then fainter and ever fainter. Tomorrow night came black, then day again, night again, day again, faster and faster still. An eddying murmur filled my ears, and a strange, dumb confusedness descended on my mind.

I am afraid I cannot convey the peculiar sensations of time travelling. They are excessively unpleasant. There is a feeling exactly like that one has upon a road's switchback – of a helpless headlong motion! I felt the same horrible anticipation, too, of an imminent smash. As I put on pace, night followed day like the flapping of a black wing. The dim suggestion of the laboratory seemed presently to fall away from me, and I saw the sun hopping swiftly across the sky, leaping it every minute, and every minute marking a day. The twinkling succession of darkness and light was painful to the eye. Then, in the intermittent darknesses, I saw the moon spinning swiftly through her quarters from new to full, and had a faint glimpse of the circling stars. Presently, as I went on, still gaining velocity, the palpitation of night and day merged into one continuous greyness; the sky took on a wonderful deepness of blue, a splendid luminous colour like that of early twilight; the jerking sun became a streak of fire, a brilliant arch in space; the moon a fainter fluctuating band; and I could see nothing of the stars, save now and then a brighter circle flickering in the blue.

The landscape was misty and vague. I was still on the hillside upon which this house now stands, and the shoulder rose above me grey and dim. I saw trees growing and changing like puffs of vapour, now brown, now green; they grew, spread, shivered, and passed away. I saw huge buildings rise up faint and fair, and pass like dreams. The whole surface of the earth seemed changed – melting and flowing under my eyes. The little hands upon the dials that registered my speed raced round faster and faster. Presently I noted that the sun belt swayed up and down, from solstice to solstice, in a minute or less, and that consequently my pace was over a year a minute; and minute by minute the white snow flashed across the world, and vanished, and was followed by the bright, brief green of spring.

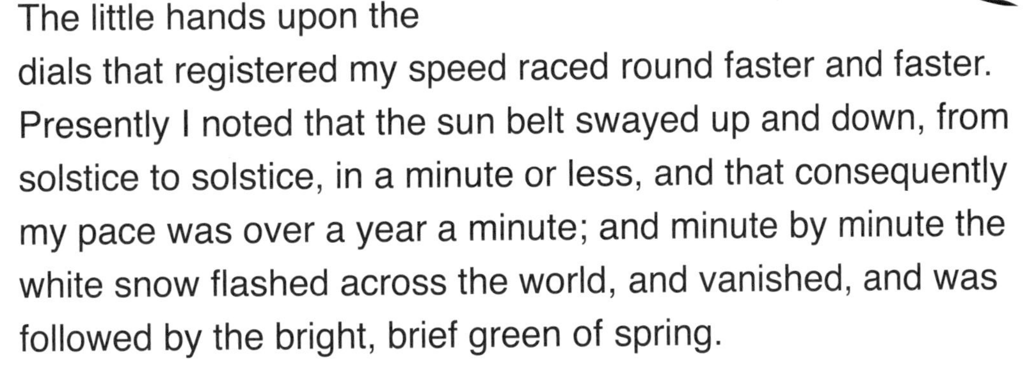

The unpleasant sensations of the start were less powerful now. They merged at last into a kind of hysterical exhilaration. I remarked, indeed, a clumsy swaying of the machine, for which I was unable to account. But my mind was too confused to attend to it, so with a kind of madness growing upon me, I flung myself into the future. At first I scarce thought of stopping, scarce thought of anything but these new sensations. But presently a fresh series of impressions grew up in my mind – a certain curiosity and therewith a certain dread – until at last they took complete possession of me. What strange developments of humanity, what wonderful advances upon our rudimentary civilisation, I thought, might appear when I came to look closely into the dim elusive world that raced and fluctuated before my eyes! I saw great and splendid architecture rising about me, more massive than any buildings of our own time, and yet, as it seemed, built of glimmer and mist. I saw a richer green flow up the hillside, and remain there, without any wintry intermission. Even through the veil of my confusion the earth seemed very fair. And so my mind came round to the business of stopping.

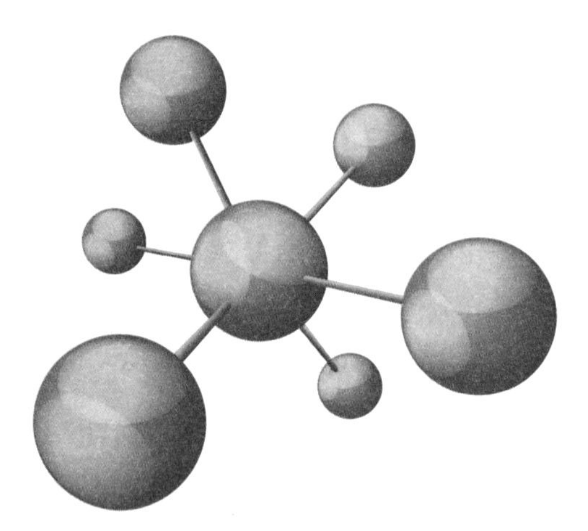

The greatest risk lay in the possibility of my finding some substance in the space which I, or the machine, occupied. So long as I travelled at a high velocity through time, this scarcely mattered. But to come to a stop involved the jamming of myself, molecule by molecule, into whatever lay in my way; meant bringing my atoms into such intimate contact with those of the obstacle that a profound chemical reaction – possibly a far-reaching explosion – would result, and blow myself and my apparatus out of all possible dimensions, into the unknown. This possibility had occurred to me again and again while I was making the machine; but then I had cheerfully accepted it as an unavoidable risk – one of the risks a man has got to take! Now the risk was inevitable, I no longer saw it in the same cheerful light. The fact is that the absolute strangeness of everything, the sickly jarring and swaying of the machine, and above all, the feeling of prolonged falling, had upset my nerves. I told myself that I could never stop, but with a gust of petulance I decided to stop immediately.

Like an impatient fool, I tugged the lever, and …

Some of the language in this story is quite old-fashioned, but I hope you can see why I've chosen it.

Wells imagines the experience of time travelling so perfectly that it seems real, taking us into the fears and hopes of the traveller – so that it's easy to imagine ourselves in his place.

The extract ends in a way that leaves almost any option open!

YOUR CONTINUATION

Before I overwhelm you with advice, why not have a go at writing a continuation without any interference from me?

Bear in mind that your job isn't to finish the story: you just have to write the next part of it.

Like an impatient fool, I tugged the lever, and ....

....

....

....

....

....

....

....

....

....

....

....

....

HOW NOT TO DO IT

Because there are so many ways to continue a story well, let's start by thinking about how you might do it badly.

If you can learn how to make a mess on purpose, you'll be less likely to do it by accident! **At least, that's the theory ...**

Mistake 1: Taking the plot where it doesn't want to go

There are many directions in which you might take this story. However, it's still possible to introduce plot twists that make your reader think "**What's going on? That wouldn't happen!**"

See whether you can write a continuation weird enough to leave your reader scratching their head – but try to maintain the style and tone of the original text as far as you can.

Like an impatient fool, I tugged the lever, and ....

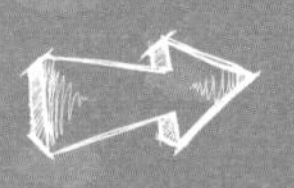

Here's my own attempt to bend Wells' plot so far that it hurts:

Like an impatient fool, I tugged the lever, and my world jarred nauseatingly. With a grinding choke, the machine barked, whined, then sighed to a halt. I shook myself and looked around.

Rolling downs were scattered with flowers, while here and there a great blue tree soared some two hundred feet into the sky. Between the trees skipped pink and blue butterflies, each wing the size of my palm. One separated itself from the rest, checked its whirligig flight and settled to hover before my face.

Where I had expected to see six insect legs, here were two hands and two minute feet. Where I had expected dull bug eyes, here was a smiling face crowned with golden braids like woven thread. And where I had expected only the whispering flutter of insect wings, here was a tiny yet determined voice: "Welcome to the fairy land, traveller."

The creature fluttered closer, its smile broadening. Now I noticed a pin-sized wand in its hand, coloured sparks flickering at its point. Then the mouth, no larger than a grain of rice, moved again: "Before you die like those who arrived before you, what is your last command?"

I flicked my own wand, and the creature exploded in a supernova of crimson flame.

This response keeps close to the writing style of H.G. Wells' text, but the fourth and fifth paragraphs take the story in a very unnatural direction.

Whereas Wells takes a fantastic idea – **travelling into the future in a home-made time machine** – and uses scientific language to make it realistic, my answer fills the story with murderous fairies. And what about the time traveller's deadly wand, which seems to appear from nowhere?

My plot development owes as much to J.K. Rowling as H.G. Wells.

Mistake 2: Distorting the character

Begin a continuation that uses the same character, but changes his personality so that he seems like a different person.

Like an impatient fool, I tugged the lever, and ....

....

....

....

....

....

....

....

....

....

....

....

....

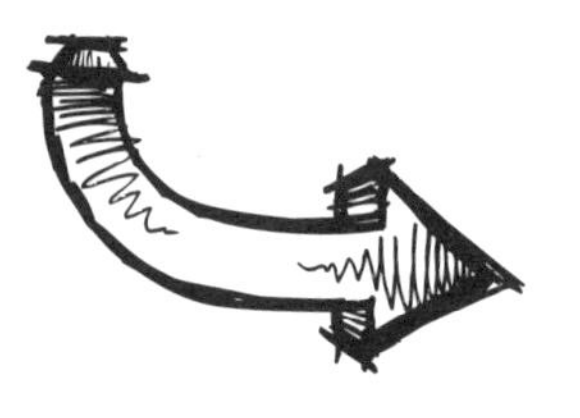

Let's see whether
I can make the
time traveller even
less recognisable
than you have!

Like an impatient fool, I tugged the lever, and the machine shook and roared. The world decelerated violently around me, and then with a crash the chair tipped, and I sprawled forwards onto hard ground. Snarling at the machine's clumsiness, I clawed myself upright and aimed a kick at its still-shuddering bulk.

I found that I had come to rest on a patch of concrete, closely surrounded by shining, four-wheeled pods of metal and glass, all lined up side by side and completely still. I craned my head, putting out a hand against the reflected glare of the sun, and allowed my eyes to track up the steel and glass lines of an enormous tower, stretching almost endlessly towards the shimmering sky.

I turned, shifting my gaze from tower to tower, until I became aware of buzzing voices. A crowd was gathering at the edge of the clearing, chattering energetically, watching me and my machine. I looked back at them without warmth. So, this was the future.

With momentary decision, I strode back to the machine, settled myself in the saddle, and reversed the lever.

We know from the original text that the traveller is fascinated by the thought of what he will encounter in the future. He wants to learn all that he can from it:

> "What strange developments of humanity, what wonderful advances upon our rudimentary civilisation, I thought, might appear."

He's especially interested in buildings, and notices the "**great and splendid architecture**" that rises around him as he travels.

In my continuation, however, he seems unimpressed by this strange world of skyscrapers and shiny cars. He takes a quick look around, then decides to go back home!

What's more, while the original traveller is able to endure "**excessively unpleasant**" experiences, yet remain focused and excited despite them, in my version he is so impatient and petulant that he takes revenge on the machine by kicking it – just because he fell to the ground when it stopped.

Mistake 3: Changing the writing style

Now have a go at changing to a radically different style, making it obvious that a different writer has taken over.

Like an impatient fool, I tugged the lever, and ....

....

....

....

There are so **many ways** to do this that my answer will probably be very different from yours. Here's my effort:

Like an impatient fool, I tugged the lever, and WHAM! I saw stars.

Then my vision settled. "Well, you could knock me down with a feather", I thought. "This is cool!"

I was on a tropical island. At least, it seemed tropical, although I'd never visited the tropics. And it seemed like an island. Mind you, my eyes could only follow the shore until it curved out of sight behind waving palm trees.

The machine had come to rest in front of a wooden hut, open on one side towards the beach. Inside it stood a man with long hair, who had, until a few seconds ago, been in the process of pouring drinks for two babes in skimpy bathing costumes.

Now a scatter of glass wobbled in a wash of spreading liquid at his feet, while his frozen hand continued to grasp a bottle-sized tube of air. All three people gawped at me.

"Hi guys," I drawled, flicking them a wave.

It's hard to imagine H.G. Wells writing about "babes", using the words "cool" and "guys", or having his protagonist "WHAM!" to a halt.

My sentence structure also creates a tone very different from that in the original passage. For instance, I use chopped up, overlapping thoughts to show the narrator's uncertainty: "**I was … At least, it seemed … And it seemed … Mind you …**"

This is quite different from the carefully ordered formality of Wells' writing. In other words, it's out of place here!

When you continue a story by another author, you have to do your best to become them – not bend things to fit your favourite approach. If you decide to mix your usual writing style with theirs,

you need to do so very carefully.

TIME TO WRITE WELL AGAIN!

At this point, it might be worth having another look at your original continuation on pages 8 to 9. Did you make any of the mistakes that we've been playing with here – even if a bit less obviously?

Whether you did or not, **now's your chance to improve on your first attempt**, or even to try a completely different approach.

Like an impatient fool, I tugged the lever, and ....

You may well be curious about how the original passage continues. Here is the next part of **The Time Machine**:

Like an impatient fool, I tugged the lever, and incontinently the thing went reeling over, and I was flung headlong through the air.

There was the sound of a clap of thunder in my ears. I may have been stunned for a moment. A pitiless hail was hissing round me, and I was sitting on soft turf in front of the overset machine. Everything still seemed grey, but presently I remarked that the confusion in my ears was gone. I looked round me. I was on what seemed to be a little lawn in a garden, surrounded by rhododendron bushes, and I noticed that their mauve and purple blossoms were dropping in a shower under the beating of the hailstones. The rebounding, dancing hail hung in a cloud over the machine, and drove along the ground like smoke. In a moment I was wet to the skin. "Fine hospitality," said I, "to a man who has travelled innumerable years to see you."

Presently I thought what a fool I was to get wet. I stood up and looked round me. A colossal figure, carved apparently in some white stone, loomed indistinctly beyond the rhododendrons through the hazy downpour. But all else of the world was invisible.

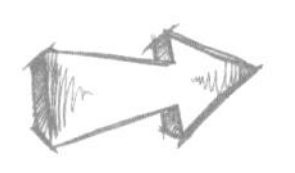

In fact, not a great deal happens in this part of Wells' story! He focuses on **describing the scene and creating atmosphere**. It's also interesting how nothing yet suggests a futuristic landscape: the grey weather and the garden plants in fact suggest a world similar to the one the traveller has left behind him.

Remember that the test of a good continuation is not whether it is **the same** as the original author's next paragraphs. Instead, what matters is:

Whether your continuation is **vivid and interesting.**

Whether your continuation **could have been written by the author.**

FOLLOW-UP EXERCISE

Here's another classic text, adapted from a very different book: Charlotte Brontë's *Jane Eyre*.

Though I had now extinguished my candle and was laid down in bed, I could not sleep for thinking of Mr Rochester's look when he paused in the avenue, and told me how his destiny had risen up before him, and dared him to be happy at Thornfield.

"Why not?" I asked myself. "What alienates him from the house? Will he leave it again soon? Mrs Fairfax said he seldom stayed here longer than a fortnight at a time; and he has now been resident eight weeks. If he does go, the change will be miserable. Suppose he should be absent spring, summer, and autumn: how joyless sunshine and fine days will seem!"

I hardly know whether I had slept or not after these thoughts. At any rate, I started wide awake on hearing a vague murmur, peculiar and lugubrious, which came, I thought, from just above me. I wished I had kept my candle burning: the night was drearily dark and my spirits were depressed. I rose and sat up in bed, listening. The sound was hushed.

I tried again to sleep, but my heart beat anxiously: my inward calm was broken. The clock, far down in the hall, struck two. Just then it seemed my chamber door was touched, as if fingers had swept the panels in groping a way along the dark gallery outside. I said, "Who is there?" Nothing answered. I was chilled with fear.

All at once I remembered that it might be Pilot, who, when the kitchen door chanced to be left open, not infrequently found his way up to the threshold of Mr Rochester's chamber: I had seen him lying there myself in the mornings. The idea calmed me somewhat, and I lay down. Silence composes the nerves; and as an unbroken hush now reigned again through the whole house, I began to feel the return of slumber. But it was not fated that I should sleep that night. A dream had scarcely approached my ear, when it fled in fright.

There was a demoniac laugh – low, suppressed, and deep – uttered, as it seemed, at the very keyhole of my chamber door. The head of my bed was near the door, and I thought at first the goblin-laugher stood at my bedside – or rather, crouched by my pillow: but I rose, looked round, and could see nothing. As I still gazed, the unnatural sound was reiterated, and I knew it came from behind the panels. My first impulse was to rise and fasten the bolt; my next, again to cry out, "Who is there?"

Something gurgled and moaned. Before long, steps retreated up the gallery towards the third-storey staircase. A door had lately been made to shut in that staircase. I heard it open and close, and all was still.

"Was that Grace Poole? And is she possessed with a devil?" thought I. It was impossible now to remain by myself: I must go to Mrs Fairfax. I hurried on my frock and a shawl. I withdrew the bolt and opened the door with a trembling hand. There was a candle burning just outside, and on the matting in the gallery. I was surprised at this circumstance: but still more was I amazed to perceive the air quite dim, as if filled with smoke. While looking to the right hand and left, to find whence these blue wreaths issued, I became further aware of a strong smell of burning.

Something creaked: it was a door ajar; and that door was Mr Rochester's, and the smoke rushed from it in a cloud.

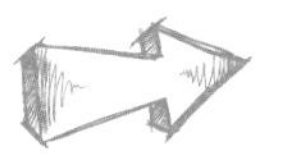

Have a go at continuing this story in an effective way.

Match your style to Brontë's as best you can. Try to move the plot in a natural and interesting direction, and keep exploring the character of the narrator, Jane Eyre – without turning her into a different person!

Something creaked: it was a door ajar; and that door was Mr Rochester's, and the smoke rushed from it in a cloud.

....

....

....

....

....

....

....

....

Here is Charlotte Brontë's own continuation, for you to compare. It's a wonderful example of what you might do, even though some of the language is old-fashioned.

Remember, however, that your work can be wildly different and still excellent.

Something creaked: it was a door ajar; and that door was Mr Rochester's, and the smoke rushed from it in a cloud.

I thought no more of Mrs Fairfax. I thought no more of Grace Poole, or the laugh. In an instant, I was within the chamber. Tongues of flame darted round the bed: the curtains were on fire. In the midst of blaze and vapour, Mr Rochester lay stretched motionless, in deep sleep.

"Wake! Wake!" I cried. I shook him, but he only murmured and turned: the smoke had stupefied him. Not a moment could be lost: the very sheets were kindling. I rushed to his basin and jug. Fortunately, one was wide and the other deep, and both were filled with water. I heaved them up, deluged the bed and its occupant, flew back to my own room, brought my own water jug, baptized the couch afresh, and, by God's aid, succeeded in extinguishing the flames which were devouring it.

The hiss of the quenched fire, the breakage of a pitcher which I flung from my hand when I had emptied it, and, above all, the splash of the shower bath I had liberally bestowed, roused Mr Rochester at last. Though it was now dark, I knew he was awake, because I heard him fulminating strange curses at finding himself lying in a pool of water.

"Is there a flood?" he cried.

"No, sir," I answered, "but there has been a fire. Get up, do! You are quenched now. I will fetch you a candle."

"In the name of all the elves in Christendom, is that Jane Eyre?" he demanded. "What have you done with me, witch, sorceress? Who is in the room besides you? Have you plotted to drown me?"

MAKING YOUR OWN PRACTICE EXERCISES

Now that you've had lots of practice with these passages, you can easily create your own tasks!

- Stop reading one of your favourite books at an interesting point. Hide the rest of the page.
- See whether you can continue it in your own way, developing the characters and experimenting with the author's writing style.
- Compare your work to what the author themselves did.

If you set yourself an exercise like this every few weeks, it's likely that your writing will improve enormously.

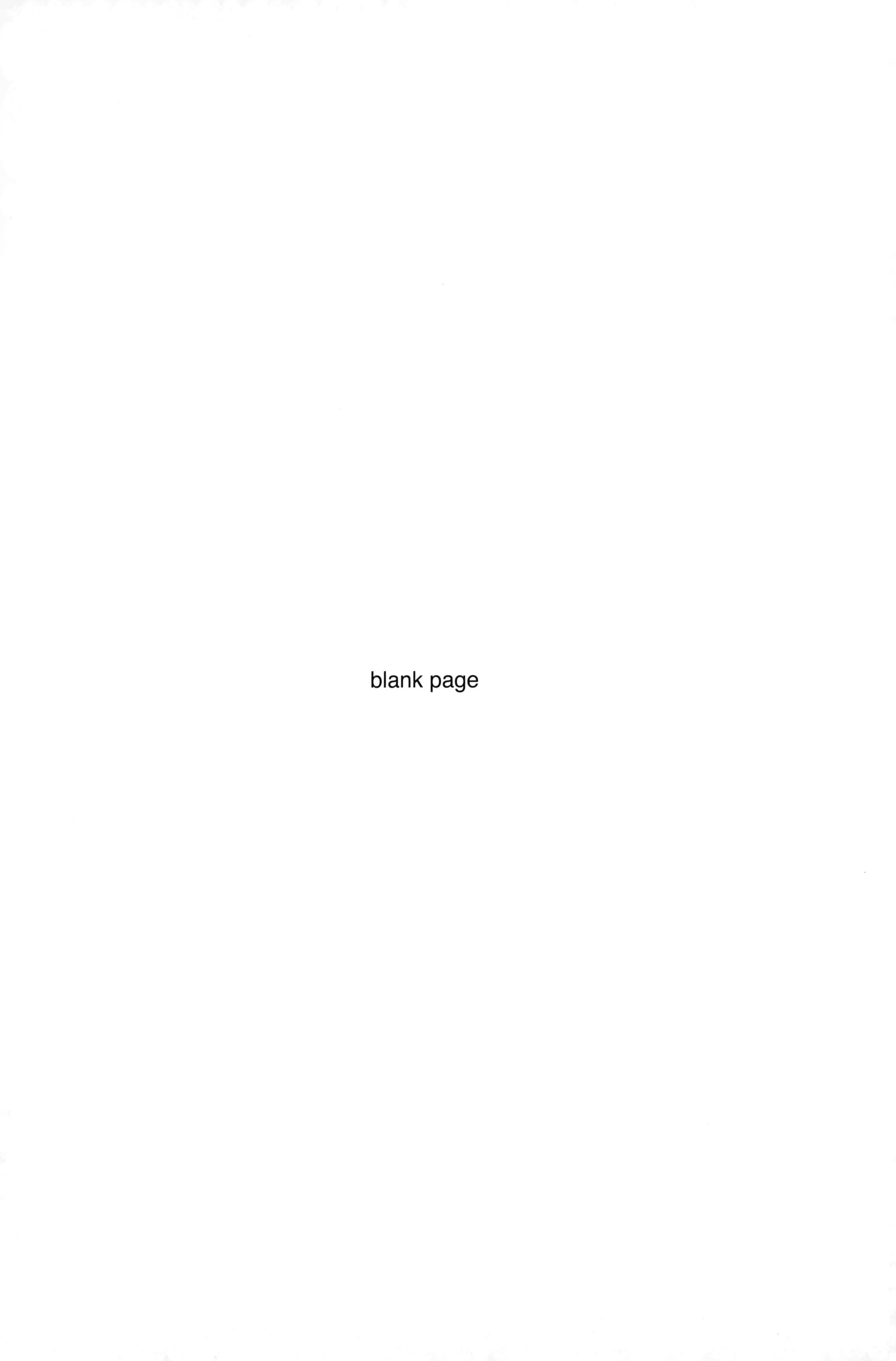

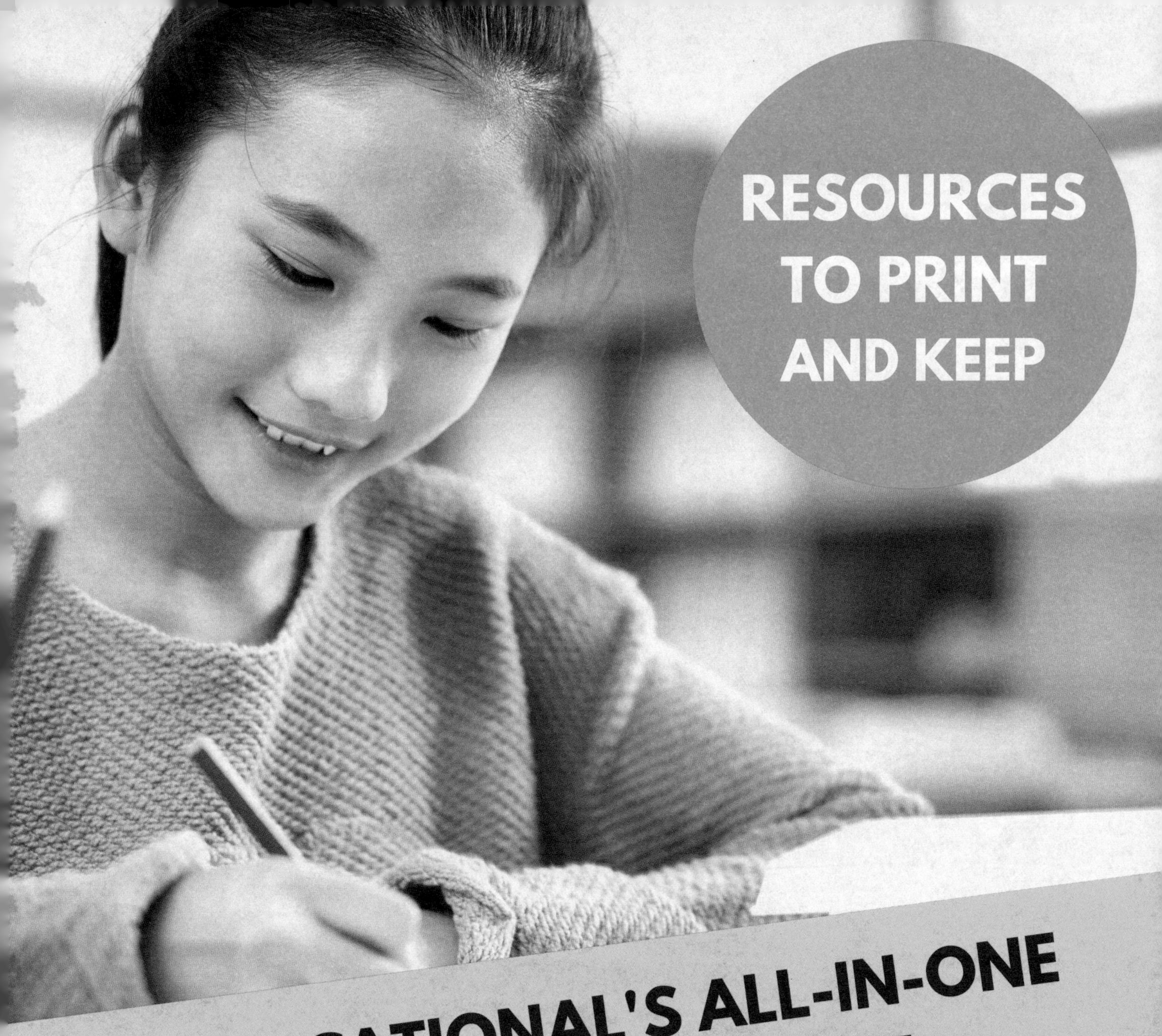
RESOURCES
TO PRINT
AND KEEP